Marguerite de Angeli's

BOOK OF
FAVORITE HYMNS

DOUBLEDAY & COMPANY, INC.

Garden City, New York

ACKNOWLEDGMENTS

"All Things Bright and Beautiful" (Royal Oak), adapted by Martin Shaw. Reprinted by permission of J. Curwen & Sons Limited. "O Beautiful for Spacious Skies" from "America the Beautiful" Katherine Lee Bates. From the book *Poems* by Katherine Lee Bates. Published by E. P. Dutton & Company, Inc., and reprinted with their permission. "O Lord, Turn Not Thy Face from Them" from Hymn 11, "Lent" by Vincent Persichetti. Permission for reprint from *Hymns and Responses for the Church Year* granted by Elkan-Vogel Co., Inc., copyright owners, Philadelphia, Pa. "Once to Every Man and Nation" (Ebenezer). Reprinted by permission of Gwenlyn Evans Limited. "For the Beauty of the Earth" from "England's Lane" adapted by Geoffrey Shaw. Reprinted by permission of Oxford University Press. "Dear Lord and Father of Mankind" Nikolaus Hermann. Reprinted by permission of Psalms and Hymns Trust. "The Old Rugged Cross" George Bennard. Reprinted by permission of The Rodeheaver Hall-Mack Co.

Contents

INDEX OF TITLES 4

Praise God from Whom All Blessings Flow (Doxology) 7

I Think When I Read That Sweet Story of Old 8

A Mighty Fortress Is Our God 10

The King of Love My Shepherd Is 11

I Need Thee Every Hour 12

Rock of Ages 13

Lead, Kindly Light 14

There Is a Green Hill Far Away (Easter) 15

Lead On, O King Eternal 16

Sun of My Soul 17

O Little Town of Bethlehem (Christmas) 18

Away in a Manger (Christmas) 19

O Come, All Ye Faithful (Christmas) 20

Angels, from the Realms of Glory (Christmas) 21

Blest Be the Tie That Binds 22

Saviour, Again to Thy Dear Name 23

As Pants the Hart 24

O Master, Let Me Walk with Thee 25

Jesus Loves Me 26

Jesus, Tender Shepherd, Hear Me 27

Holy, Holy, Holy 29

Dear Lord and Father of Mankind 30

Come, Thou Almighty King 31

All Things Bright and Beautiful 32

O Beautiful for Spacious Skies 34

Faith of Our Fathers 35

Fairest Lord Jesus 36

O Love That Wilt Not Let Me Go 37

I Love to Tell the Story 38

Father, We Thank Thee for the Night 40

"Welcome, Happy Morning!" (Easter) 41

Jesus Christ Is Risen Today (Easter) 42

Crown Him with Many Crowns 43

Come, Ye Thankful People, Come (Thanksgiving) 44

The Old Rugged Cross (Easter) 46

O God, Our Help in Ages Past 47

For the Beauty of the Earth 48

God of Our Fathers 49

O Perfect Love 50

He Leadeth Me 52

O Lord, Turn Not Thy Face from Them (Lent) 53

How Firm a Foundation 54

Jerusalem the Golden 55

We Gather Together (Thanksgiving) 56

Wake, Awake, for Night Is Flying 58

Love Divine, All Love Excelling 60

Abide with Me 61

Saviour, Like a Shepherd Lead Us 62

Once to Every Man and Nation 63

Now the Day Is Over 64

Index of Titles

4

Abide with Me	61
All Things Bright and Beautiful	32
A Mighty Fortress Is Our God	10
Angels, from the Realms of Glory	21
As Pants the Hart	24
Away in a Manger	19
Blest Be the Tie That Binds	22
Come, Thou Almighty King	31
Come, Ye Thankful People, Come	44
Crown Him with Many Crowns	43
Dear Lord and Father of Mankind	30
Fairest Lord Jesus	36
Faith of Our Fathers	35
Father, We Thank Thee for the Night	40
For the Beauty of the Earth	48
God of Our Fathers	49
He Leadeth Me	52
Holy, Holy, Holy	29
How Firm a Foundation	54
I Love to Tell the Story	38
I Need Thee Every Hour	12
I Think When I Read That Sweet Story of Old	8
Jerusalem the Golden	55
Jesus Christ Is Risen Today	42
Jesus Loves Me	26
Jesus, Tender Shepherd, Hear Me	27
King of Love My Shepherd Is, The	11
Lead, Kindly Light	14
Lead On, O King Eternal	16
Love Divine, All Love Excelling	60
Now the Day Is Over	64
O Beautiful for Spacious Skies	34
O Come, All Ye Faithful	20
O God, Our Help in Ages Past	47
Old Rugged Cross, The	46
O Little Town of Bethlehem	18
O Lord, Turn Not Thy Face from Them	53
O Love That Wilt Not Let Me Go	37
O Master, Let Me Walk with Thee	25
Once to Every Man and Nation	63
O Perfect Love	50
Praise God from Whom All Blessings Flow	7
Rock of Ages	13
Saviour, Again to Thy Dear Name	23
Saviour, Like a Shepherd Lead Us	62
Sun of My Soul	17
There Is a Green Hill Far Away	15
Wake, Awake, for Night Is Flying	58
We Gather Together	56
"Welcome, Happy Morning!"	41

Foreword

This small collection of hymns contains many of my favorites. Some among them are not my choice, but have been included because they are favorites of my friends and of many to whom I have spoken.

Hymns must be as old as man himself, for even among the people we call primitive there are chants or hymns expressing joy or grief.

When one experiences what Elizabeth Vining calls "the minor ecstasies" because of the exquisite beauty of a child, the perfection of a rose, a sunset, or a leaf, reminding us of their Creator, a hymn goes up from a heart too full for speech to the All-Knowing, in thankfulness or in need.

My first memory of hymns is the sound of my mother's voice, singing as she comforted me for some childish hurt. It may even have been to comfort herself: to quiet her spirit while some crisis passed. All through her life she sang when troubled, as if to keep her serenity before her children.

In a time when there was neither radio nor television, it was the custom in many homes, ours among them, to gather round the piano and sing hymns. It was a lovely custom and I wish it were more common now. In my parents' household, often, as we were busy about the house and in different rooms, one of us would start a hymn, then it would be taken up by another and another in harmony till we were all singing.

Perhaps one of the charms of singing hymns is that they are usually sung in company. Good group or congregational singing is inspiring and lifts the heart.

Once, when my grandfather was quite old, he and I sang a duet together at a church service. The hymn we sang, "O Perfect Love," is among those following, and I found it in his hymn book.

MARGUERITE DE ANGELI

Other Books by Marguerite de Angeli

BLACK FOX OF LORNE

BOOK OF NURSERY AND MOTHER GOOSE RHYMES

BRIGHT APRIL

COPPER-TOED BOOTS

THE DOOR IN THE WALL

ELIN'S AMERIKA

HENNER'S LYDIA

JARED'S ISLAND

JUST LIKE DAVID

THE OLD TESTAMENT

PETITE SUZANNE

A POCKET FULL OF POSIES

SKIPPACK SCHOOL

TED AND NINA GO TO THE GROCERY STORE

THEE, HANNAH!

YONIE WONDERNOSE

Praise God from Whom All Blessings Flow

L. BURGEOIS

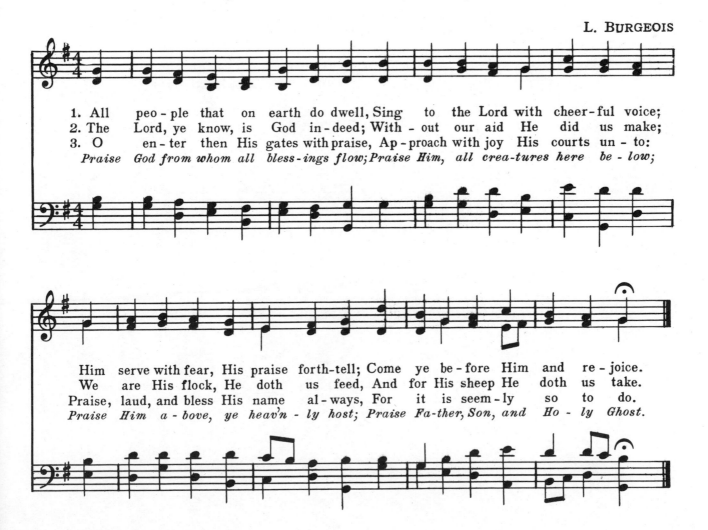

1. All peo-ple that on earth do dwell, Sing to the Lord with cheer-ful voice;
2. The Lord, ye know, is God in-deed; With-out our aid He did us make;
3. O en-ter then His gates with praise, Ap-proach with joy His courts un-to:

Praise God from whom all bless-ings flow; Praise Him, all crea-tures here be-low;

Him serve with fear, His praise forth-tell; Come ye be-fore Him and re-joice.
We are His flock, He doth us feed, And for His sheep He doth us take.
Praise, laud, and bless His name al-ways, For it is seem-ly so to do.

Praise Him a-bove, ye heav'n-ly host; Praise Fa-ther, Son, and Ho-ly Ghost.

I Think When I Read That Sweet Story of Old

MRS. JEMIMA LUKE   WILLIAM BRADBURY

8

1. I think when I read that sweet sto-ry of old, When Je-sus was here a-mong men, How He called lit-tle chil-dren as lambs to His fold, I should like to have been with them then.

2. I wish that His hands had been placed on my head, That His arm had been thrown a-round me, And that I might have seen His kind look when He said, "Let the lit-tle ones come un-to Me."

3. Yet still to His foot-stool in prayer I may go, And ask for a share in His love; And if I now ear-nest-ly seek Him be-low, I shall see Him and hear Him a-bove.

4. But thou-sands and thou-sands who wan-der and fall Nev-er heard of that heav-en-ly home; I should like them to know there is room for them all, And that Je-sus has bid them to come.

5. I long for the joy of that glo-ri-ous time, The sweet-est and bright-est and best, When the dear lit-tle chil-dren of ev-er-y clime Shall crowd to His arms and be blest. A-men.

A Mighty Fortress Is Our God

MARTIN LUTHER
Translation by F.H. HEDGE

MARTIN LUTHER

10

1. A might-y for-tress is our God, A bul-wark nev-er fail-ing;
2. Did we in our own strength con-fide, Our striv-ing would be los-ing,
3. And though this world, with dev-ils filled, Should threat-en to un-do us,
4. That word a-bove all earth-ly powers, No thanks to them, a-bid-eth;

Our help-er he a-mid the flood Of mor-tal ills pre-vail-ing.
Were not the right man on our side, The man of God's own choos-ing.
We will not fear, for God hath willed His truth to tri-umph through us.
The Spir-it and the gifts are ours Through him who with us sid-eth.

For still our an-cient foe Doth seek to work us woe; His craft and power are
Dost ask who that may be? Christ Je-sus, it is he; Lord Sab-a-oth his
The prince of dark-ness grim, We trem-ble not for him; His rage we can en-
Let goods and kin-dred go, This mor-tal life al-so; The bod-y they may

great, And armed with cru-el hate, On earth is not his e-qual.
name. From age to age the same, And he must win the bat-tle.
dure, For lo, his doom is sure: One lit-tle word shall fell him.
kill; God's truth a-bid-eth still, His king-dom is for-ev-er. A-men.

11

The King of Love My Shepherd Is

HENRY W. BAKER   JOHN B. DYKES

1. The King of love my Shep-herd is, Whose good-ness fail-eth nev-er;
2. Where streams of liv-ing wa-ter flow, My ran-somed soul He lead-eth,
3. Per-verse and fool-ish oft I strayed, But yet in love He sought me,
4. In death's dark vale I fear no ill With Thee, dear Lord, be-side me;
5. And so through all the length of days, Thy good-ness fail-eth nev-er;

I noth-ing lack if I am His, And He is mine for-ev-er.
And, where the ver-dent pas-tures grow, With food ce-les-tial feed-eth.
And on His shoul-der gen-tly laid, And home, re-joic-ing, brought me.
Thy rod and staff my com-fort still, Thy cross be-fore to guide me.
Good Shep-herd, may I sing Thy praise With-in Thy house for-ev-er.

I Need Thee Every Hour

ANNIE S. HAWKS

ROBERT LOWRY

1. I need Thee ev-'ry hour, Most gra - cious Lord; No ten - der voice like
2. I need Thee ev-'ry hour, Stay Thou near by; Temp - ta - tions lose their
3. I need Thee ev-'ry hour, In joy or pain; Come quick - ly and a -
4. I need Thee ev-'ry hour, Most Ho - ly One; O make me Thine in -

CHORUS

Thine Can peace af - ford.
pow'r When Thou art nigh.
bide, Or life is vain.
deed, Thou bless - ed Son!

I need Thee, O I need Thee; Ev - 'ry hour I

need Thee! O bless me now, my Sav - ior, I come to Thee!

12

Rock of Ages

AUGUST TOPLADY

THOMAS HASTINGS

13

1. Rock of A - ges, cleft for me, Let me hide my - self in Thee;
2. Could my tears for ev - er flow, Could my zeal no lan - guor know,
3. While I draw this fleet - ing breath, When my eyes shall close in death,

Let the wa - ter and the blood, From Thy wound - ed side which flowed,
These for sin could not a - tone; Thou must save, and Thou a - lone:
When I rise to worlds un - known, And be - hold Thee on Thy throne,

Be of sin the dou - ble cure, Save from wrath and make me pure.
In my hand no price I bring, Sim - ply to Thy cross I cling.
Rock of A - ges cleft for me, Let me hide my - self in Thee.

Lead, Kindly Light

JOHN NEWMAN

JOHN B. DYKES

14

1. Lead, kind-ly Light, a-midth' en - cir-cling gloom, Lead Thou me on;
2. I was not ev - er thus, nor prayed that Thou Shouldst lead me on;
3. So long Thy power hath blest me, sure it still Will lead me on,

The night is dark, and I am far from home; Lead Thou me on:
I loved to choose and see my path; but now Lead Thou me on.
O'er moor and fen, o'er crag and tor-rent, till The night is gone;

Keep Thou my feet; I do not ask to see
I loved the gar - ish day, and, spite of fears,
And with the morn those an gel fac - es smile,

The dis - tant scene one step e - nough for me.
Pride ruled my will: re - mem - ber not past years.
Which I have loved long since, and lost a - while. A - men.

There Is a Green Hill Far Away

C.F. ALEXANDER

S. WEBBE

1. There is a green hill far a - way, With-out a cit - y wall,
2. We may not know, we can - not tell, What pains He had to bear,
3. He died that we might be for - given, He died to make us good,
4. There was no oth - er good e - nough To pay the price of sin,
5. Oh, dear - ly, dear - ly has He loved! And we must love Him too,

Where the dear Lord was cru - ci - fied, Who died to save us all.
But we be - lieve it was for us He hung and suf - fered there.
That we might go at last to heaven, Saved by His pre - cious blood.
He on - ly could un - lock the gate Of heav'n, and let us in.
And trust in His re - deem - ing blood, And try His works to do.

A - men.

Lead On, O King Eternal

16

Sun of My Soul

JOHN KEBLE

WILLIAM MONK

1. Sun of my soul! Thou Sav - iour dear, It is not
2. When the soft dews of kind - ly sleep My wea - ry
3. A - bide with me from morn till eve, For with - out
4. Be near to bless me when I wake, Ere thro' the

night if Thou be near; Oh, may no earth - born
eye - lids gen - tly steep, Be my last tho't how
Thee I can - not live; A - bide with me when
world my way I take; A - bide with me till

17

cloud a - rise To hide Thee from Thy ser - vant's eyes!
sweet to rest For - ev - er on my Sav - ior's breast!
night is nigh, For with - out Thee I dare not die.
in Thy love I lose my - self in heav'n a - bove.

O Little Town of Bethlehem

Away in a Manger

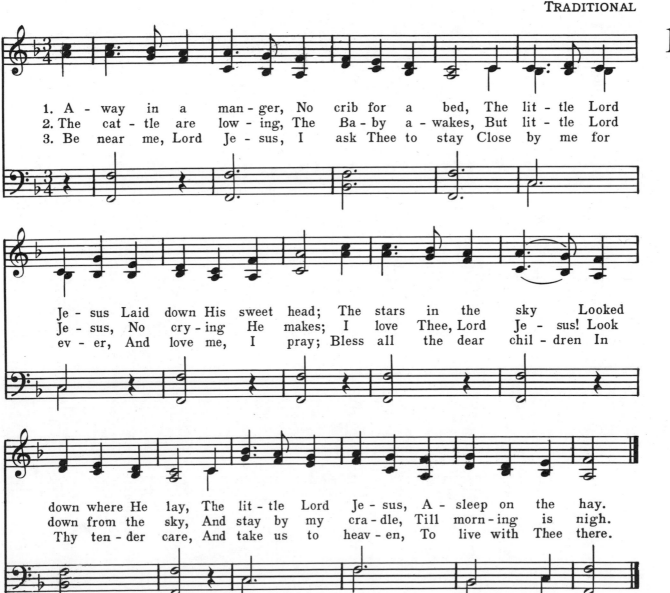

1. A - way in a man - ger, No crib for a bed, The lit - tle Lord
2. The cat - tle are low - ing, The Ba - by a - wakes, But lit - tle Lord
3. Be near me, Lord Je - sus, I ask Thee to stay Close by me for

Je - sus Laid down His sweet head; The stars in the sky Looked
Je - sus, No cry - ing He makes; I love Thee, Lord Je - sus! Look
ev - er, And love me, I pray; Bless all the dear chil - dren In

down where He lay, The lit - tle Lord Je - sus, A - sleep on the hay.
down from the sky, And stay by my cra - dle, Till morn - ing is nigh.
Thy ten - der care, And take us to heav - en, To live with Thee there.

O Come, All Ye Faithful

Translation of *Adeste Fideles* by F. OAKLEY

TRADITIONAL

20

1. O come, all ye faith-ful, joy-ful and tri-um-phant, O
2. Sing, choirs of an-gels, sing in ex-ul-ta-tion, O
3. Yea, Lord, we greet Thee, born this hap-py morn-ing,

come ye, O come ye to Beth-le-hem; Come and be-hold Him,
sing, all ye bright hosts of heav'n a-bove; Glo-ry to God, all
Je-sus, to Thee be all glo-ry giv'n; Word of the Fa-ther,

REFRAIN

born the King of an-gels.
glo-ry in the high-est. O come, let us a-dore Him, O come, let us a-
now in flesh ap-pear-ing.

dore Him, O come, let us a-dore Him, Christ, the Lord. A-men.

Angels, from the Realms of Glory

JAMES MONTGOMERY

HENRY SMART

1. An-gels, from the realms of glo-ry, Wing your flight o'er all the earth;
2. Shep-herds, in the field a-bid-ing, Watch-ing o'er your flocks by night,
3. Saints, be-fore the al-ter bend-ing, Watch-ing long in hope and fear,

Ye who sang cre-a-tion's sto-ry, Now pro-claim Mes-si-ah's birth:
God with man is now re-sid-ing; Yon-der shines the in-fant light:
Sud-den-ly the Lord de-scend-ing, In His tem-ple shall ap-pear:

Come and wor-ship, come and wor-ship, Wor-ship Christ, the new-born King. A-men.

Blest Be the Tie That Binds

JOHN FAWCETT

HANS NAGALI

1. Blest be the tie that binds Our hearts in Christian love; The
2. Before our Father's throne, We pour our ardent pray'rs; Our
3. We share our mutual woes, Our mutual burdens bear; And
4. When we asunder part, It gives us inward pain; But

fellowship of kindred minds Is like to that above.
fears, our hopes, our aims are one, Our comforts and our cares.
often for each other flows The sympathizing tear.
we shall still be joined in heart, And hope to meet again.

22

Saviour, Again to Thy Dear Name

John Ellerton

E. J. Hopkins

1. Sav-iour, a-gain to Thy dear name we raise With one ac-cord our part-ing hymn of praise; We stand to bless Thee ere our wor-ship cease; Then, low-ly kneel-ing, wait Thy word of peace.

2. Grant us Thy peace up-on our home-ward way; With Thee be-gan, with Thee shall end the day; Guard Thou the lips from sin, the hearts from shame, That in this house have called up-on Thy name.

3. Grant us Thy peace, Lord, through the com-ing night; Turn Thou for us its dark-ness in-to light; From harm and dan-ger keep Thy chil-dren free, For dark and light are both a-like to Thee.

4. Grant us Thy peace through-out our earth-ly life, Our balm in sor-row, and our stay in strife; Then, when Thy voice shall bid our con-flict cease, Call us, O Lord, to Thine e-ter-nal peace.

A - men.

23

As Pants the Hart

HUGH WILSON
har. by ROBERT A. SMITH

With dignity

24

1. As pants the hart for cool - ing streams When heat - ed in the chase,
2. For thee, my God, the liv - ing God, My thirst - y soul doth pine:
3. Why rest - less, why cast down, my soul? Hope still, and thou shalt sing
4. To Fa - ther, Son, and Ho - ly Ghost, The God whom we a - dore,

So longs my soul, O God, for thee, And thy re - fresh - ing grace.
O when shall I be - hold thy face, Thou Ma - jes - ty di - vine?
The praise of him who is thy God, Thy health's e - ter - nal spring.
Be glo - ry, as it was, is now, And shall be ev - er - more. A-men.

O Master, Let Me Walk with Thee

WASHINGTON GLADDEN   HENRY P. SMITH

1. O Mas-ter, let me walk with Thee In low-ly paths of serv-ice free;
2. Help me the slow of heart to move By some clear, win-ning word of love;
3. Teach me Thy pa-tience; still with Thee In clos-er, dear-er com-pa-ny,
4. In hope that sends a shin-ing ray Far down the fu-ture's broad-'ning way;

Tell me Thy se-cret; help me bear The strain of toil, the fret of care.
Teach me the way-ward feet to stay, And guide them in the home-ward way.
In work that keeps faith sweet and strong, In trust that tri-umphs o-ver wrong.
In peace that on-ly Thou canst give, With Thee, O Mas-ter, let me live.

Jesus Loves Me

ANNA B. WARNER

WILLIAM BRADBURY

26

1. Je-sus loves me! this I know, For the Bi - ble tells me so;
2. Je-sus loves me! He who died, Heav - en's gate to o - pen wide;
3. Je-sus loves me! loves me still, Though I'm ver - y weak and ill;
4. Je-sus loves me! He will stay Close be - side me all the way;

CHORUS

Lit - tle ones to Him be-long; They are weak, but He is strong.
He will wash a - way my sin, Let His lit - tle child come in.
From His shin - ing throne on high, Comes to watch me where I lie. Yes, Je-sus
If I love Him, when I die He will take me home on high.

loves me, Yes, Je-sus loves me, Yes, Je-sus loves me_ The Bi-ble tells me so.

Jesus, Tender Shepherd, Hear Me

MARY DUNCAN

JOHN STAINER

In unison, simply

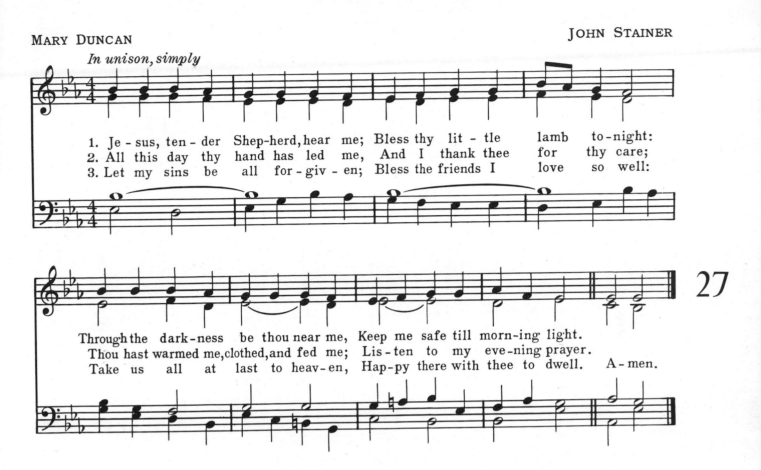

1. Je - sus, ten - der Shep-herd, hear me; Bless thy lit - tle lamb to-night:
2. All this day thy hand has led me, And I thank thee for thy care;
3. Let my sins be all for - giv - en; Bless the friends I love so well:

Through the dark-ness be thou near me, Keep me safe till morn-ing light.
Thou hast warmed me, clothed, and fed me; Lis-ten to my eve-ning prayer.
Take us all at last to heav-en, Hap-py there with thee to dwell. A - men.

Holy, Holy, Holy

REGINALD HEBER

JOHN B. DYKES

1. Ho - ly, ho - ly, ho - ly! Lord God Al - might - y!
2. Ho - ly, ho - ly, ho - ly! all the saints a - dore Thee,
3. Ho - ly, ho - ly, ho - ly! Lord God Al - might - y!

Ear - ly in the morn - ing our song shall rise to Thee;
Cast - ing down their gold - en crowns a - round the glass - y sea;
All Thy works shall praise Thy name, in earth, and sky, and sea;

29

Ho - ly, ho - ly, ho - ly, mer - ci - ful and might - y!
Cher - u - bim and sera - phim fall - ing down be - fore Thee,
Ho - ly, ho - ly, ho - ly, mer - ci - ful and might - y!

God in Three Per - sons, bless - ed Trin - i - ty!
Which wert, and art, and ev - er - more shalt be.
God in Three Per - sons, bless - ed Trin - i - ty! A - men.

Dear Lord and Father of Mankind

JOHN GREENLEAF WHITTIER

FREDERICK C. MAKER

30

1. Dear Lord and Fa - ther of man-kind, For - give our fool - ish ways.
2. In sim - ple trust like theirs who heard, Be - side the Syr - ian sea,
3. O sab - bath rest by Gal - i - lee! O calm of hills a - bove!
4. Drop thy still dews of qui - et-ness, Till all our striv - ings cease;
5. Breathe through the puls - es of de - sire Thy cool - ness and thy balm;

Re - clothe us in our right - ful mind; In pur - er lives thy
The gra - cious call - ing of the Lord, Let us, like them, with
Where Je - sus knelt to share with thee The si - lence of e -
Take from our souls the strain and stress, And let our or - dered
Let sense be dumb, let flesh re - tire: Speak through the earth-quake,

serv - ice find, In deep - er rev - erence, praise.
out a word, Rise up and fol - low thee.
ter - ni - ty, In - ter - pret - ed by love.
lives con - fess The beau - ty of thy peace.
wind, and fire, O still, small voice of calm. A - men.

Come, Thou Almighty King

ANONYMOUS

FELICE GIARDINI

31

1. Come, thou Al - might - y King, Help us Thy name to sing,
2. Come, thou in - car - nate Word, Gird on Thy might - y sword,
3. Come, ho - ly Com - fort - er, Thy sa - cred wit - ness bear
4. To the great One in Three, E - ter - nal prais - es be

Help us to praise: Fa - ther, all glo - ri - ous, O'er all vic -
Our prayer at - tend: Come, and Thy peo - ple bless, And give Thy
In this glad hour: Thou who al - might - y art, Now rule in
Hence ev - er - more. His sov - 'reign ma - jes - ty May we in

to - ri - ous, Come, and reign o - ver us An - cient of Days.
word suc - cess; Spir - it of ho - li - ness, On us de - scend.
ev - 'ry heart, And ne'er from us de - part, Spir - it of power.
glo - ry see, And to e - ter - ni - ty Love and a - dore. A - men.

All Things Bright and Beautiful

CECIL FRANCES ALEXANDER

Traditional English Melody,
adapted by MARTIN SHAW

REFRAIN *Cheerfully*

All things bright and beau - ti - ful, All crea-tures great and small,

All things wise and won - der - ful, The Lord God made them all.

Stanzas commence here

1. Each lit - tle flower that o - pens, Each lit - tle bird that sings,
2. The pur - ple head - ed moun-tain, The riv - er run - ning by,
3. The cold wind in the win - ter, The plea - sant sum - mer sun,
4. He gave us eyes to see them, And lips that we might tell

He made their glow-ing col - ors, He made their ti - ny wings.
The sun - set, and the morn - ing That bright-ens up the sky,
The ripe fruits in the gar - den, He made them ev - 'ry one.
How great is God Al - migh - ty, Who has made all things well.

33

O Beautiful for Spacious Skies

KATHERINE LEE BATES

SAMUEL A. WARD

34

1. O beau-ti-ful for spa-cious skies, For am-ber waves of grain,
2. O beau-ti-ful for pil-grim feet, Whose stern, im-pas-sioned stress
3. O beau-ti-ful for pa-triot dream That sees, be-yond the years,

For pur-ple moun-tain maj-es-ties A-bove the fruit-ed plain!
A thor-ough-fare for free-dom beat A-cross the wil-der-ness!
Thine al-a-bas-ter cit-ies gleam, Un-dimmed by hu-man tears!

A-mer-i-ca! A-mer-i-ca! God shed His grace on thee,
A-mer-i-ca! A-mer-i-ca! God mend thine ev-ery flaw,
A-mer-i-ca! A-mer-i-ca! God shed His grace on thee,

And crown thy good with broth-er-hood From sea to shin-ing sea.
Con-firm thy soul in self-con-trol, Thy lib-er-ty in law.
And crown thy good with broth-er-hood From sea to shin-ing sea. A-men.

Faith of Our Fathers

FREDERICK W. FABER

H. F. HEMY
Arranged by J. G. WALTON

35

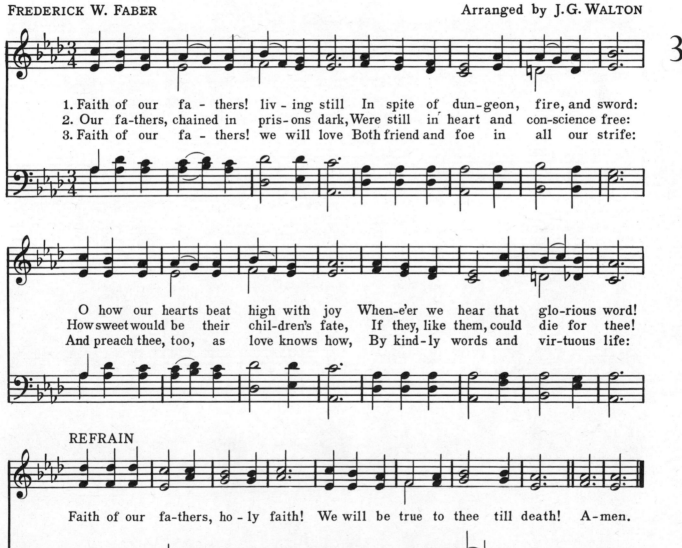

1. Faith of our fa - thers! liv - ing still In spite of dun - geon, fire, and sword:
2. Our fa - thers, chained in pris - ons dark, Were still in heart and con-science free:
3. Faith of our fa - thers! we will love Both friend and foe in all our strife:

O how our hearts beat high with joy When-e'er we hear that glo-rious word!
How sweet would be their chil-dren's fate, If they, like them, could die for thee!
And preach thee, too, as love knows how, By kind-ly words and vir-tuous life:

REFRAIN

Faith of our fa-thers, ho - ly faith! We will be true to thee till death! A-men.

Fairest Lord Jesus

TRADITIONAL

36

1. Fair - est Lord Je - sus! Rul - er of all na - ture!
2. Fair are the mead - ows, Fair - er still the wood - lands,
3. Fair is the sun - shine, Fair - er still the moon - light,

O Thou of God and man the Son! Thee will I cher - ish,
Robed in the bloom - ing garb of spring; Je - sus is fair - er,
And all the twink - ling star - ry host; Je - sus shines bright - er,

Thee will I hon - or, Thou, my soul's glo - ry, joy, and crown!
Je - sus is pur - er, Who makes the woe - ful heart to sing!
Je - sus shines pur - er, Than all the an - gels heav'n can boast! A - men.

O Love That Wilt Not Let Me Go

GEORGE MATHESON   ALBERT PEACE

37

1. O Love that wilt not let me go, I
2. O Light that fol - l'west all my way, I
3. O Joy that seek - est me through pain, I
4. O Cross that lift - est up my head, I

rest my wea - ry soul in Thee; I give Thee back the life I owe,
yield my flick-'ring torch to Thee; My heart re - stores its bor-rowed ray,
can not close my heart to Thee; I trace the rain-bow thro' the rain,
dare not ask to fly from Thee; I lay in dust life's glo - ry dead,

That in Thine o - cean depths its flow May rich - er, full - er be.
That in Thy sun-shine's blaze its day May bright - er, fair - er be.
And feel the prom - ise is not vain That morn shall tear - less be.
And from the ground there blos-soms red Life that shall end-less be. A-men.

38

I Love to Tell the Story

KATHERINE HANKEY   WILLIAM G. FISCHER

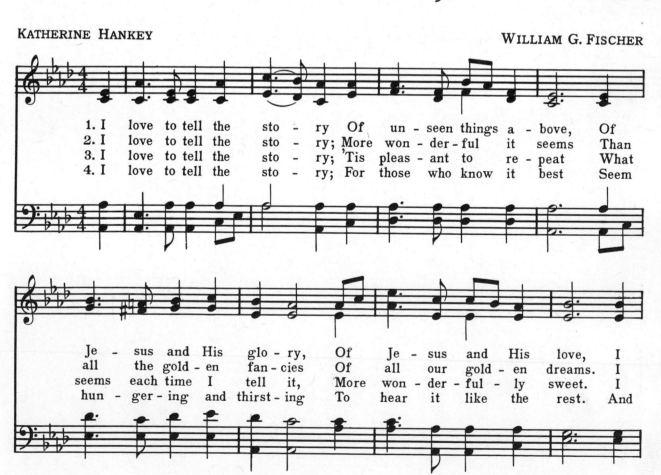

1. I love to tell the sto - ry Of un - seen things a - bove, Of
2. I love to tell the sto - ry; More won - der - ful it seems Than
3. I love to tell the sto - ry; 'Tis pleas - ant to re - peat What
4. I love to tell the sto - ry; For those who know it best Seem

Je - sus and His glo - ry, Of Je - sus and His love, I
all the gold - en fan - cies Of all our gold - en dreams. I
seems each time I tell it, More won - der - ful - ly sweet. I
hun - ger - ing and thirst - ing To hear it like the rest. And

Father, We Thank Thee for the Night

REBECCA J. WESTON

DANIEL BATCHELLOR

40

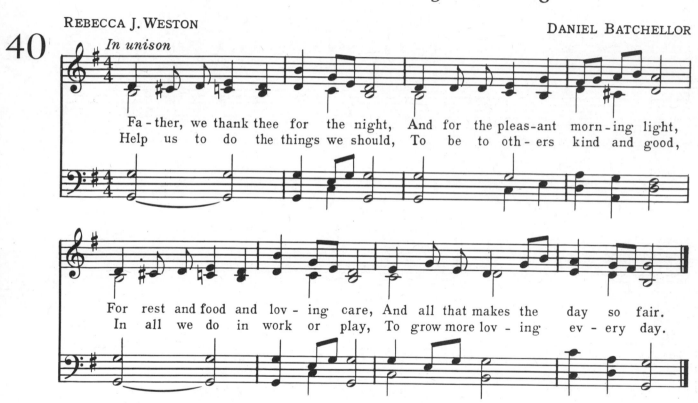

Fa-ther, we thank thee for the night, And for the pleas-ant morn-ing light,
Help us to do the things we should, To be to oth-ers kind and good,

For rest and food and lov-ing care, And all that makes the day so fair.
In all we do in work or play, To grow more lov-ing ev-ery day.

"Welcome, Happy Morning!"

ARTHUR SEYMOUR SULLIVAN

With animation

1. "Wel - come, hap - py morn - ing!" age to age shall say:
2. Earth her joy con - fess - es, cloth - ing her for spring,

Hell to - day is van - quished, heav'n is won to - day!
All fresh gifts re - turned with her re - turn - ing King:

Lo! the dead is liv - ing, God for ev - er - more!
Bloom in ev - 'ry mea - dow, leaves on ev - 'ry bough,

Him, their true Cre - a - tor, all his works a - dore!
Speak his sor - row end - ed, hail his tri - umph now.

41

Jesus Christ Is Risen Today

UNKNOWN

1. "Je - sus Christ is ris'n to - day," Al - le - lu - ia!
2. Lives a - gain our glo - rious King: Al - le - lu - ia!
3. Sing we to our God a - bove; Al - le - lu - ia!

Sons of men and an - gels say: Al - le - lu - ia!
Where, O death, is now thy sting? Al - le - lu - ia!
Praise e - ter - nal as His love; Al - le - lu - ia!

Raise your joys and tri - umphs high, Al - le - lu - ia!
Dy - ing once He all doth save: Al - le - lu - ia!
Praise Him all ye heaven - ly host, Al - le - lu - ia!

Sing, ye heav'ns, and earth re - ply, Al - le - lu - ia!
Where thy vic - to - ry, O grave? Al - le - lu - ia!
Fa - ther, Son and Ho - ly Ghost; Al - le - lu - ia!

42

Crown Him with Many Crowns

MATHEW BRIDGES

GEORGE ELVEY

1. Crown Him with man - y crowns, The Lamb up - on His throne;
2. Crown Him the Lord of love! Be - hold His hands and side,
3. Crown Him the Lord of Heav'n! One with the Fa - ther known,

Hark! how the heav'n - ly an - them drowns All mu - sic but its own!
Rich wounds, yet vis - i - ble a - bove, In beau - ty glo - ri - fied:
One with the Spir - it through Him giv'n From yon - der glo - rious throne!

43

A - wake, my soul, and sing Of Him who died for thee, And
No an - gel in the sky Can ful - ly bear that sight, But
To Thee be end - less praise, For Thou for us hast died; Be

hail Him as thy match - less King Thro' all e - ter - ni - ty.
down - ward bends his won - d'ring eye At mys - ter - ies so bright.
Thou, O Lord, thro' end - less days A - dored and mag - ni - fied. A - men.

Come, Ye Thankful People, Come

HENRY ALFORD   GEORGE ELVEY

44

1. Come, ye thank-ful peo-ple, come, Raise the song of har-vest home:
2. All the world is God's own field, Fruit un-to His praise to yield;
3. For the Lord our God shall come, And shall take His har-vest home;
4. E-ven so, Lord, quick-ly come To Thy fi-nal har-vest home;

All is safe-ly gath-ered in, Ere the win-ter storms be-gin;
Wheat and tares to-geth-er sown, Un-to joy or sor-row grown;
From His field shall in that day All of-fens-es purge a-way;
Gath-er Thou Thy peo-ple in, Free from sor-row, free from sin;

God, our Ma-ker, doth pro-vide For our wants to be sup-plied:
First the blade, and then the ear, Then the full corn shall ap-pear:
Give His an-gels charge at last In the fire the tares to cast;
There, for-ev-er pu-ri-fied, In Thy pres-ence to a-bide:

Come to God's own tem-ple, come, Raise the song of har-vest home.
Lord of har-vest, grant that we Whole-some grain and pure may be.
But the fruit-ful ears to store In His gar-ner ev-er-more.
Come, with all Thine an-gels, come, Raise the glo-rious har-vest home.

The Old Rugged Cross

GEORGE BENNARD

GEORGE BENNARD

46

1. On a hill far a-way stood an old rug-ged cross, The em - blem of
2. In the old rug-ged cross, stained with blood so di - vine, A won - drous
3. To the old rug-ged cross I will ev - er be true, It's shame and re -

suf-f'ring and shame; And I love that old cross where the dear-est and best
beau-ty I see; For 'twas on that old cross Je - sus suf-fered and died
proach glad-ly bear; Then He'll call me some day to my home far a - way,

CHORUS

For a world of lost sin-ners was slain.
To par - don and sanc-ti - fy me. So I'll cher-ish the old rug-ged
Where His glo - ry for - ev - er I'll share.

cross, Till my tro-phies at last I lay down; I will cling to the

old rug-ged cross, And ex-change it some day for a crown,

47

O God, Our Help in Ages Past

ISAAC WATTS

WILLIAM CROFT

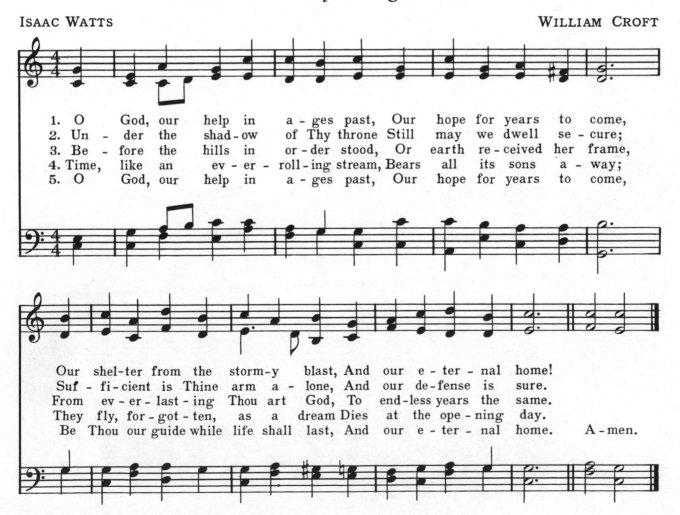

1. O God, our help in a-ges past, Our hope for years to come,
2. Un - der the shad-ow of Thy throne Still may we dwell se - cure;
3. Be - fore the hills in or-der stood, Or earth re-ceived her frame,
4. Time, like an ev-er-roll-ing stream, Bears all its sons a - way;
5. O God, our help in a-ges past, Our hope for years to come,

Our shel-ter from the storm-y blast, And our e-ter-nal home!
Suf - fi-cient is Thine arm a - lone, And our de-fense is sure.
From ev-er-last-ing Thou art God, To end-less years the same.
They fly, for-got-ten, as a dream Dies at the ope-ning day.
Be Thou our guide while life shall last, And our e-ter-nal home. A-men.

For the Beauty of the Earth

Traditional English Melody,
adapted by GEOFFREY SHAW

With spirit; may be sung in unison

48

1. For the beau-ty of the earth, For the beau-ty of the skies,
2. For the beau-ty of each hour Of the day and of the night,
3. For the joy of ear and eye, For the heart and mind's de-light,
4. For the joy of hu-man love, Broth-er, sis-ter, par-ent, child,
5. For each per-fect gift of thine To our race so free-ly giv'n,

For the love which from our birth O-ver and a-round us lies,
Hill and vale, and tree and flower, Sun and moon, and stars of light,
For the mys-tic har-mo-ny Link-ing sense to sound and sight,
Friends on earth, and friends a-bove, For all gen-tle thoughts and mild,
Grac-es hu-man and di-vine, Flowers of earth and buds of heav'n,

REFRAIN

Lord of all, to thee we raise This our hymn of grate-ful praise. A-men.

God of Our Fathers

Daniel C. Roberts

George Warren

49

Trumpets, before each verse

1. God of our fa - thers, whose al - might - y
2. Thy love di - vine hath led us in the
3. Re - fresh thy peo - ple on their toil - some

hand   Leads forth in beau - ty   all the star - ry band
past,   In this free land by   thee our lot is cast;
way,   Lead us from night to   nev - er - end - ing day;

Of   shin - ing worlds   in splen - dor through the   skies,
Be   thou our   rul - er,   guard - ian, guide and   stay,
Fill   all our lives   with love and grace di -   vine,

Our   grate - ful   songs be - fore thy throne a - rise.
Thy   word our   law, thy paths our   cho - sen way.
And   glo - ry,   laud and praise be ev - er thine.   A - men.

50

O Perfect Love

DOROTHY F. GURNEY

JOSEPH BARNBY

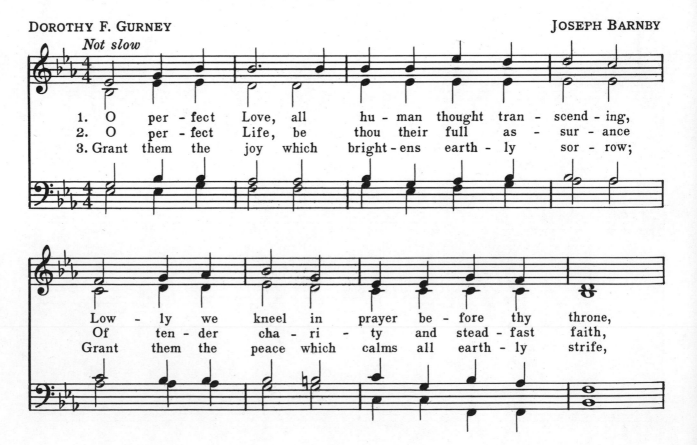

1. O per - fect Love, all hu - man thought tran - scend - ing,
2. O per - fect Life, be thou their full as - sur - ance
3. Grant them the joy which bright - ens earth - ly sor - row;

Low - ly we kneel in prayer be - fore thy throne,
Of ten - der cha - ri - ty and stead - fast faith,
Grant them the peace which calms all earth - ly strife,

That theirs may be the love that knows no end - ing,
Of pa - tient hope, and qui - et brave en - dur - ance,
And to life's day the glo - rious un - known mor - row

Whom thou for ev - er - more dost join in one.
With child - like trust that fears nor pain nor death.
That dawns up - on e - ter - nal love and life. A - men.

51

He Leadeth Me

JOSEPH H. GILMORE

WILLIAM BRADBURY

1. He lead-eth me! O bless-ed tho't! O words with heav'n-ly com-fort fraught!
2. Some-times 'mid scenes of deep-est gloom, Some-times where E - den's bow-ers bloom,
3. Lord, I would clasp Thy hand in mine, Nor ev - er mur - mur nor re-pine,
4. And when my task on earth is done, When, by Thy grace, the vic-try's won,

52

What - e'er I do, wher - e'er I be, Still 'tis God's hand that lead-eth me.
By wa - ters still, o'er troub-led sea, Still 'tis His hand that lead-eth me!
Con - tent what-ev - er lot I see, Since 'tis my God that lead-eth me!
E'en death's cold wave I will not flee, Since God thro' Jor - dan lead-eth me.

REFRAIN

He lead-eth me, He lead-eth me, By His own hand He lead-eth me:

His faith-ful fol-lower I would be, For by His hand He lead-eth me.

O Lord, Turn Not Thy Face from Them

JOHN MARCKANT

VINCENT PERSICHETTI

Solemnly

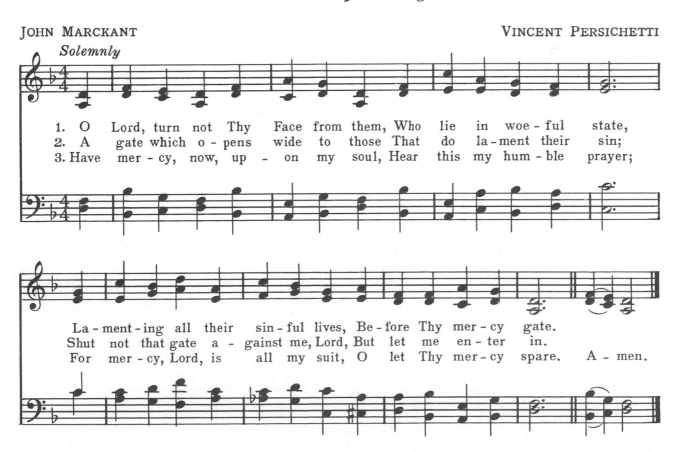

1. O Lord, turn not Thy Face from them, Who lie in woe-ful state, La-ment-ing all their sin-ful lives, Be-fore Thy mer-cy gate.
2. A gate which o-pens wide to those That do la-ment their sin; Shut not that gate a-gainst me, Lord, But let me en-ter in.
3. Have mer-cy, now, up-on my soul, Hear this my hum-ble prayer; For mer-cy, Lord, is all my suit, O let Thy mer-cy spare. A-men.

How Firm a Foundation

TRADITIONAL

ANONYMOUS

1. How firm a foun - da - tion, ye saints of the Lord, Is laid for your
2. "Fear not, I am with thee, O be not dis - mayed, For I am thy
3. "When thro' fier - y tri - als thy path - way shall lie, My grace, all suf -
4. "E'en down to old age, all My peo - ple shall prove My sov - 'reign, e -
5. "The soul that on Je - sus still leans for re - pose, I will not, I

54

faith in His ex - cel - lent Word! What more can He say, than to
God, I will still give thee aid; I'll strength - en thee, help thee, and
fi - cient, shall be thy sup - ply; The flame shall not hurt thee, I
ter - nal, un - change - a - ble love; And when hoar - y hairs shall their
will not de - sert to his foes; That soul, tho' all hell should en -

you He hath said, To you, who for ref - uge to Je - sus have fled?
cause thee to stand, Up - held by My gra - cious, om - nip - o - tent hand.
on - ly de - sign Thy dross to con - sume, and thy gold to re - fine.
tem - ples a - dorn, Like lambs they shall still in My bos - om be born.
deav - or to shake, I'll nev - er, no nev - er, no nev - er for - sake!"

Jerusalem the Golden

DR. JOHN M. NEALE

ALEXANDER C. EWING

Triumphantly

55

1. Je - ru - sa - lem the gold - en, With milk and hon - ey blest! Be -
2. They stand, those halls of Zi - on, All ju - bi - lant with song, And
3. O sweet and bless - ed coun - try, The home of God's e - lect! O

neath thy con - tem - pla - tion Sink heart and voice op - pressed. I
bright with man - y an an - gel, And all the martyr throng. The
sweet and bless - ed coun - try, That ea - ger hearts ex - pect! Je -

know not, O I know not, What joys a - wait us there! What
Prince is ev - er in them, The day - light is se - rene; The
sus, in mer - cy bring us To that dear land of rest; Who

ra - dian - cy of glo - ry, What bliss be - yond com - pare!
pas - tures of the bless - ed Are decked in glo - rious sheen.
art, with God the Fa - ther, And Spir - it, ev - er blessed. A - men.

We Gather Together

Translated from the Dutch by THEODORE BAKER   Traditional tune arranged by EDWARD KREMSER

56

1. We gath - er to - geth - er to ask the Lord's bless - ing;
2. Be - side us to guide us, our God with us join - ing,
3. We all do ex - tol Thee, Thou Lead - er tri - um - phant,

He chas - tens and has - tens His will to make known;
Or - dain - ing, main - tain - ing His king - dom di - vine;
And pray that Thou still our De - fend - er wilt be.

The wick - ed op - press - ing now cease from dis - tress - ing;
So from the be - gin - ning the fight we were win - ning;
Let Thy con - gre - ga - tion es - cape trib - u - la - tion;

Sing prais - es to His Name, He for - gets not His own.
Thou, Lord, wast at our side, all glo - ry be Thine.
Thy Name be ev - er praised! O Lord, Make us free! A - men.

Wake, Awake, for Night is Flying

PHILLIP NICOLAI
Translation by PAUL ENGLISH

PHILLIP NICOLAI
Harmonized by JOHANN SEBASTIAN BACH

58

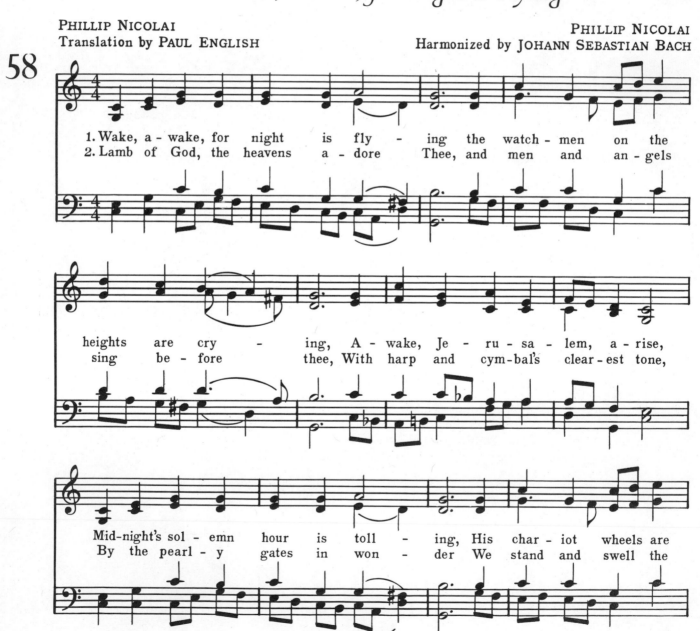

1. Wake, a-wake, for night is fly - ing the watch - men on the heights are cry - ing, A-wake, Je-ru-sa-lem, a-rise, Mid-night's sol-emn hour is toll - ing, His char-iot wheels are
2. Lamb of God, the heavens a-dore Thee, and men and an-gels sing be-fore thee, With harp and cym-bal's clear-est tone, By the pearl-y gates in won - der We stand and swell the

near - er roll - - ing, He comes; pre - pare, ye vir - gins, wise. Rise
voice of thun - - der, That ech - oes round Thy dazz-ling throne. No

up with will - ing feet. Go forth, the bride - groom meet. Al - le - lu - ia! Bear
vi - sion ev - er brought, No ear hath ev - er caught such bliss and joy. We

thru the night your well trimmed light, speed forth to join the mar-riage rite.
raise the song, we swell the throng, to praise Thee a - ges all a - long. A-men.

Love Divine, All Love Excelling

CHARLES WESLEY

JOHN ZUNDEL

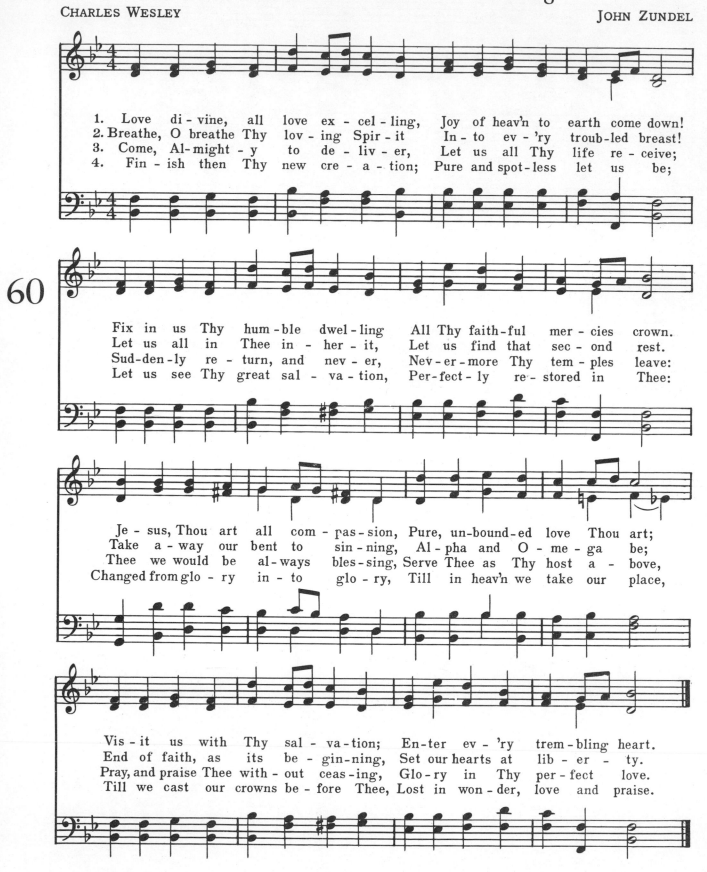

1. Love di - vine, all love ex - cel - ling, Joy of heav'n to earth come down!
2. Breathe, O breathe Thy lov - ing Spir - it In - to ev - 'ry troub - led breast!
3. Come, Al - might - y to de - liv - er, Let us all Thy life re - ceive;
4. Fin - ish then Thy new cre - a - tion; Pure and spot - less let us be;

60

Fix in us Thy hum - ble dwel - ling, All Thy faith - ful mer - cies crown.
Let us all in Thee in - her - it, Let us find that sec - ond rest.
Sud - den - ly re - turn, and nev - er, Nev - er - more Thy tem - ples leave:
Let us see Thy great sal - va - tion, Per - fect - ly re - stored in Thee:

Je - sus, Thou art all com - pas - sion, Pure, un - bound - ed love Thou art;
Take a - way our bent to sin - ning, Al - pha and O - me - ga be;
Thee we would be al - ways bles - sing, Serve Thee as Thy host a - bove,
Changed from glo - ry in - to glo - ry, Till in heav'n we take our place,

Vis - it us with Thy sal - va - tion; En - ter ev - 'ry trem - bling heart.
End of faith, as its be - gin - ning, Set our hearts at lib - er - ty.
Pray, and praise Thee with - out ceas - ing, Glo - ry in Thy per - fect love.
Till we cast our crowns be - fore Thee, Lost in won - der, love and praise.

Abide with Me

HENRY FRANCIS LYTE

WILLIAM H. MONK

61

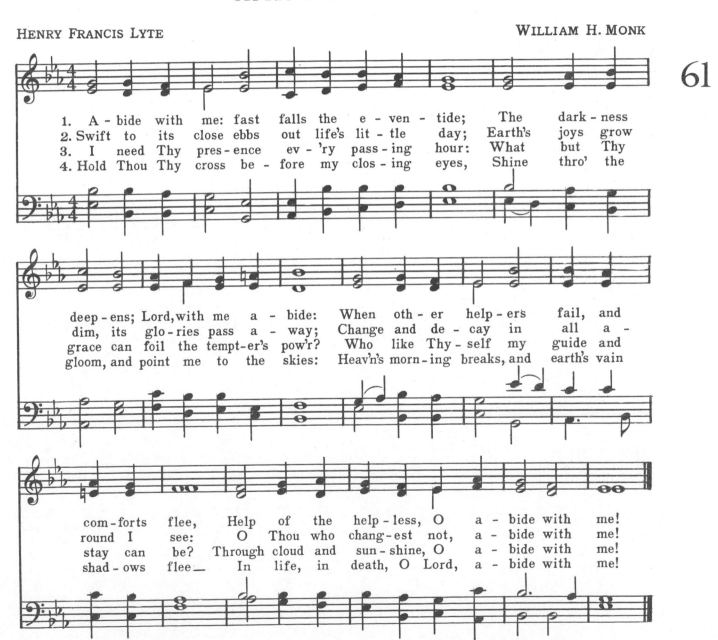

1. A - bide with me: fast falls the e - ven - tide; The dark - ness
2. Swift to its close ebbs out life's lit - tle day; Earth's joys grow
3. I need Thy pres - ence ev - 'ry pass - ing hour: What but Thy
4. Hold Thou Thy cross be - fore my clos - ing eyes, Shine thro' the

deep - ens; Lord, with me a - bide: When oth - er help - ers fail, and
dim, its glo - ries pass a - way; Change and de - cay in all a -
grace can foil the tempt - er's pow'r? Who like Thy - self my guide and
gloom, and point me to the skies: Heav'n's morn - ing breaks, and earth's vain

com - forts flee, Help of the help - less, O a - bide with me!
round I see: O Thou who chang - est not, a - bide with me!
stay can be? Through cloud and sun - shine, O a - bide with me!
shad - ows flee — In life, in death, O Lord, a - bide with me!

Saviour, Like a Shepherd Lead Us

DOROTHY THRUPP

WILLIAM BRADBURY

62

1. Sav-iour, like a Shep-herd lead us, Much we need Thy ten-der care;
2. We are Thine, do Thou be - friend us, Be the Guard-ian of our way;
3. Thou hast prom-ised to re - ceive us, Poor and sin - ful tho' we be;
4. Ear - ly let us seek Thy fa - vor; Ear - ly let us do Thy will;

In Thy pleas-ant pas-tures feed us, For our use Thy folds pre - pare:
Keep Thy flock, from sin de - fend us, Seek us when we go a-stray:
Thou hast mer - cy to re - lieve us, Grace to cleanse, and pow'r to free:
Bless - ed Lord, and on - ly Sav - iour, With Thy love our bos-oms fill:

Bless - ed Je - sus, Bless-ed Je - sus, Thou hast bought us, Thine we are;
Bless - ed Je - sus, Bless-ed Je - sus, Hear Thy chil - dren when they pray;
Bless - ed Je - sus, Bless-ed Je - sus, Ear - ly let us turn to Thee;
Bless - ed Je - sus, Bless-ed Je - sus, Thou hast loved us, love us still;

Bless - ed Je - sus, Bless-ed Je - sus, Thou hast bought us, Thine we are.
Bless - ed Je - sus, Bless-ed Je - sus, Hear Thy chil - dren when they pray.
Bless - ed Je - sus, Bless-ed Je - sus, Ear - ly let us turn to Thee.
Bless - ed Je - sus, Bless-ed Je - sus, Thou hast loved us, love us still.

Once to Every Man and Nation

James Russell Lowell

Thomas J. Williams

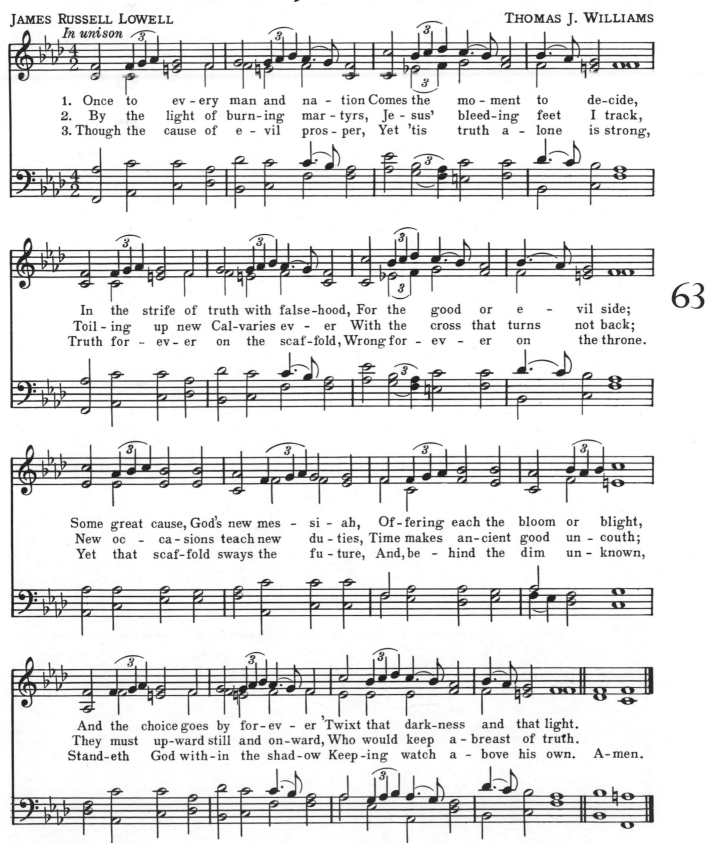

In unison

1. Once to ev-ery man and na-tion Comes the mo-ment to de-cide,
2. By the light of burn-ing mar-tyrs, Je-sus' bleed-ing feet I track,
3. Though the cause of e-vil pros-per, Yet 'tis truth a-lone is strong,

In the strife of truth with false-hood, For the good or e-vil side;
Toil-ing up new Cal-varies ev-er With the cross that turns not back;
Truth for-ev-er on the scaf-fold, Wrong for-ev-er on the throne.

Some great cause, God's new mes-si-ah, Of-fering each the bloom or blight,
New oc-ca-sions teach new du-ties, Time makes an-cient good un-couth;
Yet that scaf-fold sways the fu-ture, And, be-hind the dim un-known,

And the choice goes by for-ev-er 'Twixt that dark-ness and that light.
They must up-ward still and on-ward, Who would keep a-breast of truth.
Stand-eth God with-in the shad-ow Keep-ing watch a-bove his own. A-men.

63

64

Now the Day Is Over

SABINE BARING-GOULD

JOSEPH BARNBY

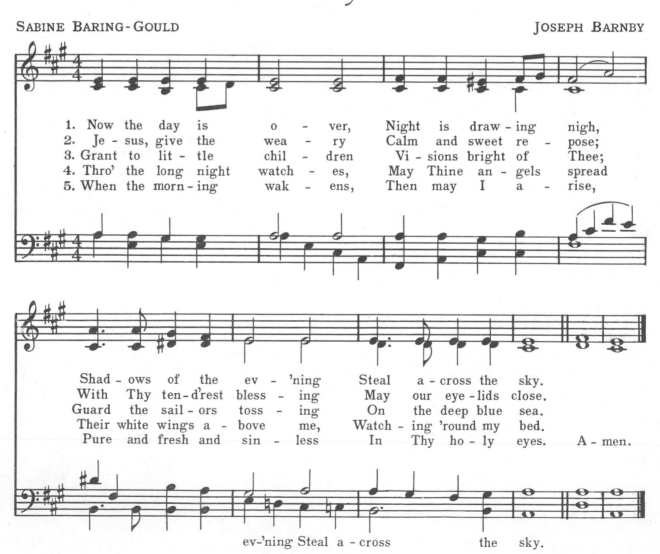

1. Now the day is o - ver, Night is draw-ing nigh,
2. Je - sus, give the wea - ry Calm and sweet re - pose;
3. Grant to lit - tle chil - dren Vi - sions bright of Thee;
4. Thro' the long night watch - es, May Thine an - gels spread
5. When the morn-ing wak - ens, Then may I a - rise,

Shad - ows of the ev - 'ning Steal a - cross the sky.
With Thy ten-d'rest bless - ing May our eye-lids close.
Guard the sail-ors toss - ing On the deep blue sea.
Their white wings a - bove me, Watch - ing 'round my bed.
Pure and fresh and sin - less In Thy ho - ly eyes. A - men.

ev-'ning Steal a - cross the sky.